The Flying Circus Mystery

Earl Thomas

High Noon Books
Novato, California

Cover Design: Michael Cincotta
Interior Illustrations: Herb Heidinger

Special thanks to Bobby Stinnett and her reading classes at Christiansburg, VA, Middle School for much help with these books.

International Standard Book Number: 0-87879-532-4

9 8 7 6 5 4
4 3 2 1 0 9 8 7 6 5

Contents

CHAPTER 1

An Exciting Job

Carlos Mendez and P.J. Turner walked into the main building of the Westside Airport. They stopped for a moment to read a large red and white sign. It was so big it covered one wall of the building

> *Come and See: Bart Mart's*
> *Flying Circus! Great Flying*
> *Stunts! Great Parachute Jumps!*
> *Three BIG Shows!!!*

The first person they saw was a tall man. They walked toward him. Carlos said to him, "We are looking for Bart Mart. Do you know him?"

The man turned to them and smiled. "You two must be Carlos and P.J. I'm Bart Mart. You called and said you are looking for work. What kind of jobs do you want?"

Carlos said, "I want an exciting job."

"What kind of jobs do you want?"

Bart smiled. "I'm not sure that we have one like that." He turned to P.J. "What kind of job do you want?"

"I'll take any job you have except a pilot's," P.J. replied.

"The pilot jobs are all filled," Bart said. "I'll be glad to give you a try at something else. It will be hard work, long hours, and much travel. Our air show moves to a different town every week, sometimes even more often. Does that sound exciting enough for you, Carlos?"

"Wow! I'll take the job, exciting or not," Carlos said.

Bart turned to P.J. "How does the job sound to you, P.J.?"

"It sounds good. But we can't start to work until next week. Watson Furniture Company, where we work now, is closing for the summer. We have a job there until Friday. After that we're free," P.J. said.

Bart replied, "Our air show operates only

during the summer. Can you report for work on Monday next week? That's when we leave Major City."

"We'll be here," Carlos said.

"Where do we report?" P.J. asked.

"Come to this office about 11 a.m.," Bart said. "I'll need to get some facts about you at that time."

As Carlos and P.J. were leaving, Bart said, "We have a show here three times during the next five days. Why don't you come to see one of them?"

"Good idea. We'll do that," Carlos said.

On Friday afternoon Carlos and P.J. said goodbye to their friends at Watson Furniture Company.

"We'll see you in two months," Carlos yelled as he and P.J. took their lunch boxes and walked away. "After a summer with the air show, we may never return."

"Carlos, you know and I know that we will

be back when the factory opens in the fall," P.J. said.

As they walked toward the apartments where they lived with their families, Carlos said, "Nobody else at the furniture factory will have such great summer jobs as we do."

"Carlos, wait until we watch the air show tomorrow. Then we'll know more. We don't really know yet what kind of job it will be," P.J. replied.

When they reached the apartments, Carlos said, "Meet me at one o'clock tomorrow. We can ride to the airfield in my car."

"Sounds good to me," P.J. said.

On Saturday afternoon when Carlos and P.J. got to the airfield, hundreds of people were there. Bart and his crew did a lot of exciting stunts. They dived and looped in their bright red planes.

Three of Bart's crew members made parachute jumps in large colorful chutes.

"Hey! Maybe we'll get to do some of those. I think this is going to be the best job in the whole world," Carlos said.

P.J. grinned. "You may be right, Carlos."

CHAPTER 2

The New Job

On Monday morning P.J. and Carlos said goodbye to their families and put their bags into P.J.'s father's car.

Mr. Turner drove them to the Westside Airport and walked into the main building with P.J. and Carlos. He shook hands and talked with Bart Mart.

Then Mr. Turner shook hands with P.J. and Carlos, "Goodbye, fellows, I hope you like the job and have a good summer."

Bart, Carlos, and P.J. walked into Bart's office. He asked them to give him more facts about their age and where they had worked before and to fill out some forms.

Then Bart said, "For today and tomorrow

we won't be doing very much. We leave in a little while for Oakville. You two will fly there with me in our largest plane. I call it the 'cruiser.' It has extra space for carrying show materials. On Wednesday in Oakville we begin to get ready for the show. That's when you will learn your jobs. Now let's go load the cruiser."

When they were outside walking toward the big white cruiser, they met the other members of the show: Phil, Hal, and Jim. All of them were pilots and did parachute tricks.

After they had loaded their bags into the planes, Carlos said to Jim, "I'll bet you have fun flying."

Jim said, "Yes, I like to fly a lot."

Carlos said quickly, "I want to learn to be a pilot. Could you teach me to fly?"

Jim said, "I'm not the one to teach you. I don't fly well enough yet to be in the show. Why don't you ask Bart or Phil or Hal? They've been flying for a long time."

P.J. walked up as Carlos was speaking and said, "Jim, you can be sure he will ask them as soon as possible."

"Thanks, Jim. Maybe I will," Carlos said.

Bart helped them to put on parachutes. He said, "This is for safety. I don't let anyone go up in one of our planes without a chute."

Then he sat in the seat behind the wheel. There was another seat beside him. He pointed to the two seats behind him for Carlos and P.J. They sat down.

Bart turned on the radio. He talked first with the pilots of the two other planes in his group. He talked with the control tower. Then he taxied his plane onto a runway.

Soon they were high in the air. Carlos and P.J. looked down. Major City seemed very small.

"Wow!" Carlos called out.

P.J. said, "Major City got smaller in just a few minutes."

Bart said, "Everything below looks smaller from up here. The only thing that gets larger is the beautiful blue sky and the clouds."

P.J. looked out the windows. Major City was soon out of sight. Now he could see hills, forests, fields, and small towns. It was a great view.

During the flight Carlos asked a lot of questions as usual. About three hours after leaving Major City, Bart landed the plane at Oakville airfield. The other two planes came close behind.

Bart and Phil made brief checks of the engines and landing gear of each plane.

Bart told Carlos and P.J., "Much of the time when we are not in the air, we are checking the planes. Anything that does not look right, sound right, or act right, we check it until it is right. We can't take any chances."

Bart walked a short distance away. Then he turned and came back. He said, "There is something else I must tell you. We have had a few strange things happen during the last month or so. We have found radio lines and the wires that supply power cut. We also found a rip in a parachute."

P.J. asked, "Have you talked to the police about this?"

Bart said, "No, not yet. But you can see why we check the planes so carefully."

"Why would somebody do these things?" P.J. asked.

"I don't know. I think it may be a young man who worked for us. He was not honest and stole some things. I fired him. That was two years ago. He might be the one who is doing these things," Bart said.

"Have you seen him around?" P.J. asked.

Bart shook his head. "No, I haven't. Phil thought he saw him at one of our recent shows but he wasn't sure. Please tell me if you see any strange people around the planes or equipment.

We haven't started to guard the planes at all hours. If we find more of these problems, we may have to take turns watching for strangers. I hope that doesn't happen but it may."

CHAPTER 3

On the Job Training

On Wednesday morning the six members of the crew worked hard to get ready for the first Oakville show. One show was to be Wednesday afternoon, the other on Thursday night.

Bart said, "Night shows are harder to do. There is more danger. Some air shows don't work at all at night."

"But you do night shows?" Carlos asked.

Bart replied, "Yes, once in a while. But people can't see as much as in the daytime show. And it's hard lighting up all the acts. Our night shows are much shorter."

The show in Oakville was to be held at a small airfield just outside of town. On Tuesday morning the crew of six went to the field.

P.J. and Carlos were told to paint long wooden pieces white and place them at spots near the field. These white pieces would be signals to the pilots and the jumpers. The jumpers were Phil, Jim, and Hal. Phil was the leader.

Phil said, "You two are very important in the jumper shows. You help to get the equipment on the right planes. You are the ones who signal us when to jump. You help keep the planes in touch on the radios. You also throw out the color stripes. During night shows you turn lights on and off at correct times. Now and then you may pack a chute, but most of the chutes are packed by the jumpers themselves."

"Wow! When will we learn to do all those things?" Carlos asked Phil.

"We begin right now," Phil said with a smile.

They began to practice doing the jobs.

The next afternoon P.J. and Carlos helped

during the show. They helped the jumpers load materials in the right planes.

In the air they threw out the long red, white, and blue strips. The strips made a pretty show of colors in the sky.

Bart told them later, "You did a nice job with the colors."

The next day everyone worked hard to get ready for the night show. Phil and Bart helped Carlos and P.J. learn all about the lighting system.

"Carlos said, "I enjoy working with lights and planes. It's exciting but I want to be a pilot."

P.J. said, "Carlos, we've got work to do. You can talk to Bart some other time about learning to fly."

Early on Thursday afternoon Bart gave Carlos and P.J. a copy of the program for the night show.

He said, "Read over the program carefully.

Notice the exact times when you need to get ready for the programs in which you are a part. The things you do must be done at exactly the right time. During trick flying I do most of the small jobs myself with lights. That's when you should be working with the chute lights and the float lights. Check everything one more time. Tonight you are doing the jobs for the first time, and the first time at night is always the hardest."

Carlos said, "Yes, sir. We know what to do."

CHAPTER 4

The First Night Show

Carlos and P.J. were excited. The night show would be hard to do. They wanted to do a good job. The lights must go on and off at exactly the right time, the right second.

If the lights were wrong, a jumper could go down in the wrong place and be hurt. P.J. and Carlos knew that they must be very careful.

The show opened with the three planes taking off. The planes were only a few feet apart as they rose into the air. The lights on the planes in the darkness made them seem closer than they were.

The crowd of people cheered as the planes went up. Carlos and P.J. flashed ground lights of many colors as the planes flew higher.

Each plane carried mixed colors of lights. The lights flashed on and off as the plane flew a loop, a roll, or a figure eight. These lights were turned on and off by the pilots. It was up to P.J. and Carlos to turn the ground lights on and off

They used bright spot lights to follow the jumpers in the sky.

at the proper times.

Many of the people liked the parachute jumps best. Phil, Jim, and Hal did their jumps very well. They did sky diving with lights, but these dives were not so clear at night as in the daylight hours.

During the jumps Carlos and P.J. were kept busy working with ground lights. They used bright spot lights to follow the jumpers in the sky. Also, the jumpers carried small colored lights to show where they were. Everyone had to be right on time or there could be a lot of problems.

Carlos and P.J. missed the lights on one jump. Phil, the leader of the jump, later told them, "Your missing the lights on that jump didn't matter. It was a safe jump. In fact, we've been thinking of dropping it from the show. You guys did a great job on all the other lights. Thank you!"

After the show Carlos and P.J. were part of

the clean-up crew. They took up wires and bulbs from all around the field. They picked up and stored safety markers. Also, they helped the pilots store the planes for the night.

Bart, Phil, Jim, and Hal moved ahead of them to walk to the van. P.J. and Carlos locked the storage room near the hangar and started to walk away.

P.J. said softly, "Carlos don't say anything yet, but somebody is moving around the outside of the hangar. Run quickly to the van and tell Bart. I'll keep watch here."

Carlos nodded and walked quickly away. Then he began to run.

P.J. watched a stranger move into the shadow of the large hangar. Its doors were locked. He asked himself, "How can he get inside if that's what he is meaning to do?"

P.J. moved closer to the hangar. Now he could see the other person at the hangar door. The stranger tried to move the large doors but he could not. He also tried the regular door. It would not open. P.J. moved closer and stood against the wall of the hangar. P.J. watched closely as the other man took a large wrench from his pocket and tapped it softly against the window in the door.

P.J. was not sure what he was doing. Was the man trying to break the window in the door? Or was he trying to break the putty around the window so he could slide the glass out?

Then P.J. heard noises behind him. He knew it was Carlos and the others. He knew that the strange man would hear them.

P.J. ran toward the man and grabbed him. The other person was strong. They fought for a moment. Then P.J. felt a hard blow on his head. He turned the man free and fell to the ground. The man ran off very fast into the darkness.

Jim and Hal took off to try to catch the stranger. Bart and Carlos stopped to help P.J.

"Who was it, P.J.?" Carlos asked.

P.J. did not answer quickly.

"Are you hurt?" Bart asked.

P.J. tried to answer both questions. "I don't know who it was. And, yes, my head hurts. I think he hit me with a wrench." He sat up and

P.J. felt a hard blow on his head.

held his head between his hands.

Jim and Hal returned. "Too bad. We lost him in the dark," Jim said.

Then Hal said, "I didn't get a good look at him. But it might have been Bob Smith. That guy who worked with us two years ago."

"If we knew for sure, we could ask the police to look for him. Of course, he didn't really do anything wrong," Bart said.

P.J. said, "He was trying to get into the hangar. He was beating on the glass in the door with a wrench."

"I don't see any damage. The window isn't broken," Bart said.

"Well, isn't it against the law to try to break in?" Carlos asked.

Bart said, "Yes, but we don't know who it was."

"We can ask the police to help us guard the planes for the few days we will be here," Phil said.

Bart said, "Good idea! I'll call the police as soon as we get back to the hotel."

Carlos said, "Bart, P.J. and I will stay here tonight if you want us to. We can sleep in the hangar with the planes."

"Thank you, Carlos. I don't think our suspect will come back tonight," Bart said.

CHAPTER 5

First Flying Lesson

Two days later the crew left Oakville for the next town, Highboro. Carlos and P.J. flew in the cruiser with Bart.

During the flight Carlos asked Bart, "How do I learn to become a pilot?"

Bart smiled and said, "You can learn quite a bit by watching what I do. I have the most important plane control in my hands now. I call it the stick. Here are some things a pilot can do with it. Watch carefully. Everything I do is important."

Bart pushed the stick forward. The plane began to dip downward. Then he pulled the stick toward him. The plane rose. He moved the stick to a middle position. The plane leveled off.

Then Bart said, "If I want to fly for a long time at this level, I push this switch. It's called the 'automatic pilot.' I don't have to handle the stick as long as the automatic pilot is on."

He turned to Carlos, "Did you see how I did those few things, Carlos?"

"Yes. Can I try them?" Carlos asked.

"Sure. Move up to the pilot's seat. I'll sit next to you," Bart said.

Carlos's face was pink and his hands were trembling as he took the pilot's seat.

Bart said, "The auto pilot is on now. Turn it off."

Carlos pushed the switch and held fast to the stick.

"Great! You remembered. Now lower our flight level by 100 feet," Bart said.

Carlos pushed the stick forward slowly. The plane began to go down. He waited a few seconds, then pulled the stick back again.

Bart said quickly, "Carlos, you did well.

But you did not watch the meter that tells us how high we are. For safety you must know how high the plane is from the ground."

"Didn't I go down 100 feet?" Carlos asked.

Bart said, "No, you went down 50 feet. Switch on the auto pilot and point to the meter that shows how high we are."

Carlos studied the meters in front of him for a moment. Then he pointed to a meter and said, "This is it. It is the altitude meter. It shows how high we are."

"Good, Carlos. Before you try to gain or lose altitude, you must always check your meter. Now try again to lose 100 feet," Bart said.

Carlos moved the switch off auto pilot. He pushed the stick slightly forward. He watched the altitude meter and then pulled the stick back again.

Bart said, "Good job, Carlos. P.J., now you try your skill behind the stick."

After P.J. and Carlos changed places, Bart said to P.J., "Do exactly what Carlos did slowly and carefully."

P.J. checked the meter that showed altitude, pushed the stick forward, watched the meter, then pulled the stick back slowly.

Bart smiled and said, "Very well done."

P.J. switched on the auto pilot and changed seats with Bart.

"Now I want you to learn to use the radio," Bart said.

First P.J. took the radio mike, pushed the ON button, and said into the mike, "This is MCB-496 calling Storm City Airport."

He repeated the call. Then he pushed the "receive" button.

Quickly the radio said, "This is Storm City. Come in MCB-496."

P.J. pushed the ON button and said, "Storm City, give us the weather report for Area 7." He pushed the "receive" button again.

The voice on the radio said, "Area 7 is clear and sunny. No weather problems."

"Thank you, Storm City," P.J. said into the mike. He switched off the mike and turned to Carlos. "O.K., Carlos, now it's your turn."

CHAPTER 6

The Stranger Again

Bart landed the cruiser at the Highboro Airport about three in the afternoon. Then he walked to the main building to wait for the other planes. P.J. and Carlos stayed with the cruiser to remove the baggage and watch over it. They were afraid the stranger might come again and try to damage the planes or equipment.

As soon as the rest of the crew arrived, P.J. said, "Let's go join the others."

They walked to the main building where Bart told each member what the schedule was for the next few days.

He said to Carlos and P.J., "Tomorrow you two will paint and place the safety markers. Be sure that every marker is in the right place.

Check them once tomorrow and again as near to show time as possible. If someone wants to cause trouble, he would most likely do it just before the show. If you see anything at all, that looks odd, tell me quickly. The life you save may be mine."

Carlos and P.J. had learned their jobs well. At each show they did their work at exactly the right time. Between shows they helped Bart and Phil with painting and repair.

On the day of the second show in Highboro, P.J. and Carlos walked around the airfield. There was a big crowd. The stands were full.

"Hey! There are a lot of people here today," Carlos said.

"Sure are," P.J. replied.

They walked toward the Food Shop. A sign on the front of the building said, "Coffee, cold drinks, sandwiches." As they came near to it, P.J. said softly, "Carlos, don't do anything different. Don't yell or holler. Over there in the door is a person who looks like the guy who hit me with the wrench. Let's go quickly and tell Bart."

Carlos looked and saw a man standing in the doorway.

They started to search for Bart in the Food Shop. Carlos and P.J. walked through the shop several times. Finally they spotted Bart drinking a cup of coffee. He also always carried hot coffee in a thermos to drink during the show. He had said, "Coffee helps keep me alert."

Carlos said, "Bart, we think we saw the guy who hit P.J. with the wrench!"

Bart stood up. "Where was he? Was he near the planes?"

"No. He was here in this building," P.J. said.

Bart said, "Let's go to the planes. We have time to make a quick check."

They ran to the hangar where the planes were parked. People who had come to see the show were standing near the planes.

Hal and Jim were making last minute checks of the landing gear.

Bart asked Jim, "Have you seen Bob Smith around here?"

"No," Jim replied.

Bart said, "P.J. thought he saw him in the Food Shop a few minutes ago. If he's here, he may try to damage the planes. Keep careful watch, Jim."

"Is it possible that he might try to do some damage to you rather than to the planes?" Jim asked.

Bart thought a moment. "I don't think so. How could he do it? Poison my food?"

Just then Phil called out, "It's time to start the show. Is everybody ready? Let's go."

P.J. said to Carlos, "Come on, Carlos. Our first job is to go up with Bart and toss out the colored strips. We can worry about that Bob Smith guy later."

They walked to the equipment shed and began to load the red, white, and blue strips into the cruiser.

From time to time they both checked to be sure no stranger was hanging around.

CHAPTER 7

A Close Call

As they climbed into the plane, P.J. looked at Bart and asked, "Bart, are you all right?"

Bart said slowly, "Yes, but I think I ate too much of that fish for supper."

"Are you well enough to fly?" P.J. asked.

"Sure. I'm not at my best but nobody is all the time," Bart said. He raised his coffee cup and took a drink.

After takeoff Bart flew the plane up to 800 feet. He did some dips, ups and downs. Carlos and P.J. tossed out strings of colored cards. They were very careful.

After tossing out the cards, Carlos and P.J. sat behind Bart. With no warning except a grunt, Bart slumped forward in the seat. Carlos yelled, "What's wrong, Bart?"

P.J. shouted, "He's passed out!"

"We'll crash! We'll die!" Carlos yelled.

"Carlos, shut up! Push Bart out of the pilot's seat and take over. I'll try to operate the

*With no warning, Bart slumped
forward in the seat.*

radio," P.J. said.

Carlos quickly pushed Bart from the pilot's seat onto the floor. Then he sat behind the controls. "Now what do I do?"

"Just remember what Bart showed us to do on the flight to Highboro. Also, look at the side of the stick. I think there are directions there for landing. Maybe they will help," P.J. said.

P.J. switched the radio to "send." He said, "Emergency! This is MCB-496 to show control. Bart has passed out!"

Then he switched the radio control to "receive." There was no sound.

He tried again. "Emergency! Emergency! Can anyone hear me?"

Then he turned to Carlos. "I don't understand what's wrong. I can't make this thing work."

"Try again, P.J.," Carlos said.

P.J. called loudly into the mike, "Phil, are

you there? Phil! Answer us please!"

No sound came from the radio. P.J. raised the mike to look at the wires. He turned to Carlos. "Our radio is dead. Two wires have been cut!"

Carlos groaned. "Oh, no! That means we're dead, too." Without thinking he leaned against the wheel, and the plane started down.

P.J. yelled, "Carlos, sit up! Pull the stick up. We've got to stay in the air for a while until we can figure how to get down without a crash."

He leaned forward and shook Bart, who was lying on the plane floor. P.J. said, "Bart, can you hear me?" There was no reply.

They were both wondering what to do. After a few moments Carlos said, "The instructions for landing are written on the stick. Read them to me, P.J."

P.J. looked on the side of the stick and said, "All right, Carlos. Keep calm. The pictures on the stick show what to do to turn the plane around and to land it."

Carlos said, "Do you think I can really land this thing?"

"Of course you can, Carlos," P.J. said.

"I'm not sure. I'm scared. My hands are shaking," Carlos said. Just then the plane dipped downward.

"Keep us level, Carlos. You just let the wheel slide forward," P.J. said.

"We can't circle around here forever. We must get down without crashing." Carlos's voice shook as he spoke.

B.J. said quickly, "Carlos, the most important thing is that we get Bart to a doctor. We don't know what is wrong with him. It may be very bad."

"O.K., I'll try to get us down," Carlos said. He moved the wheel to the left to turn the plane.

The pictures and words on the side of the stick that told how to land were:

LANDING

Gliding down to 100 feet or less . . .

Leveling off . . .

Ground contact . . .

Taxiing on the ground . . .

P.J. said, "We must do this right. Get the plane lined up with the air strip below. Move the stick a bit to the left."

"What next?" Carlos asked.

"Now start gliding down. Move the stick forward. Cut the power a little," P.J. said. He looked at the small pictures on the side of the stick.

P.J. and Carlos both watched as the plane came closer to the landing strip. It was only a few feet from the ground.

P.J. said, "Pull the stick back a little."

Carlos did so. Then they waited for the wheels to hit the ground.

"Wow!" Carlos yelled when the wheels hit.

He pulled the stick back.

The plane bounced roughly along the runway. P.J. found a stick with the word "Brake" printed on it. He pulled it. The plane slowed down more. It kept on rolling for a short distance, then stopped.

"We made it!" Carlos yelled.

Just then Bart opened his eyes and blinked slowly. He did not speak.

P.J. asked, "How are you feeling?"

Bart smiled and said slowly, "Not so good." He looked confused.

Just then Phil and another man came through the door. Phil quickly said, "Great work, you guys! I called for a doctor when I couldn't get through to you on the radio. I knew something was wrong."

The other man, carrying a small bag, sat down near Bart. He examined Bart and asked him a few questions.

"Let's go outside. Dr. Morse can take a

better look at Bart if we give him room," Phil said.

An ambulance was waiting near the plane. Phil waved a member of the crew inside to help Dr. Morse.

Bart was on a stretcher.
He waved to them.

Phil said, "I suppose the doctor will want Bart to go to the hospital for tests." Then he added with a smile, "I want to talk to you two. Most people learn to fly only after many lessons. And landing a plane is the hardest part. Yet you two had only one quick lesson, and you landed the plane perfectly. Do you know something the rest of us need to know?"

Carlos replied, "All I know is that I want to learn to fly."

"So do I. But for the next lesson I want my teacher with me," P.J. said.

Dr. Morse and the crew from the ambulance came out of the plane. They carried Bart on a stretcher. He waved to them.

Dr. Morse said to Phil, "I want to keep him in the hospital for at least one day."

"Why?" Phil asked.

"I want to make some tests that will tell us why Bart passed out. I have taken his thermos bottle and his coffee cup. Maybe we will learn something from them," Dr. Morse said.

Phil said, "Thank you, Dr. Morse. We will come to the hospital soon. First we need to talk with the police. They have picked up Bob Smith. We think he may have put knockout drops into Bart's coffee."

"We'll check the coffee that is still in the thermos." Dr. Morse said.

Then Phil turned to Carlos, "How did you get that plane down, Carlos? Was it magic?"

Carlos and P.J. laughed. Carlos said, "Yes, it was magic. The magic of wanting to stay alive."